The C...

REAGAN DIET

By Jeff Danziger

Quill / William Morrow and Co., Inc. / New York 1983

OTHER BOOKS BY JEFF DANZIGER
The Champlain Monster
The Wood-fired Automobile
The Unofficial Hunting Rules
The Vermont Mind
Out in the Sticks

ILLUSTRATED BY JEFF DANZIGER
Cat's Revenge
Cat's Revenge II
Dissolving Rubik's Cube
Everycat's Book of Eticatte
How to Make Love to a Cat
What'll You Give for It?

Library of Congress Catalog Card Number: 82-61449

ISBN: 0-688-01908-0 (pbk)

Printed in the United States of America

First Quill Edition

1   2   3   4   5   6   7   8   9   10

DEDICATED TO THE
PATRIOTIC SCHOOLCHILDREN
OF AMERICA WHO HAVE
DONATED THEIR LUNCHES
TO SAVE THE STARVING
GENERALS OF EL SALVADOR
(OR WHEREVER...)

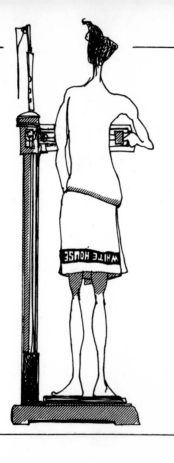

Now! At last! A great new diet for the millions of Americans who couldn't lose weight because they couldn't afford fresh fruit and Perrier. Now they can take those pounds off and keep them off!

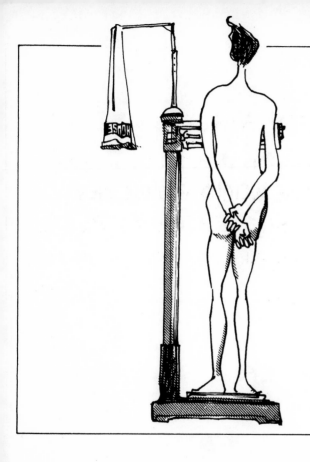

...AND WHAT IS THIS FANTASTIC NEW DIET THAT IS SWEEPING THE POVERTY POCKETS OF THE NATION?

IT'S...

The Complete
REAGAN DIET

- NO FATS
- NO PROTEINS
- NO CALORIES
- NO CLEAN WATER
- NO CLEAN AIR...

...BUT PLENTY OF
SURPLUS CHEESE!

AND WHO IS THE INVENTOR OF THIS
WONDERFUL NEW DIET? WELL, HE'S
NOT A DOCTOR, NOT FROM BEVERLY HILLS,
AND NOT A WOMAN!

HE'S RONALD REAGAN,
YOUR OWN PRESIDENT!

NATIONAL NAP
IN PROGRESS
DO NOT DISTURB
EXCEPT FOR EMERGENCY
OR MEALS

LOSING WEIGHT IS A NATIONAL OBSESSION.
SO THE FIRST THING
THE PRESIDENT DID WAS
TO LOOK FOR THE CAUSES
OF OVERWEIGHT. AND
WHAT DO YOU THINK
HE FOUND?

Overweight is caused by
FOOD STAMPS!
Overweight is caused by
WELFARE!
Overweight is caused by
PEACE OF MIND!

..and if you stay on the diet (and you will) you will see fast results. A third-generation welfare mother in Chicago found out. She went on the diet when her Food Stamps were cut off. After the first week she began to see results...

...after only two weeks she actually began to feel slimmer. She felt the pounds just melting away!
...and after just three weeks...

Well... after three weeks, she was getting positively *svelte*! There was a new look in her eye... family members noticed...

Now... she's thin and bound to stay that way! She's enjoying new, lighter, more natural foods! She's got a whole new attitude toward life.

She's a new woman!

Now, you folks out there probably have lots of questions about this new diet. So, let's go right to the Oval Office for some straight answers.

Uh... Mr. President... sir ?

PROTEIN-RICH
LOS ANGELES
AIR →

PROTEIN-RICH
NEW YORK
CITY TAP
WATER
↓

What about Protein?

Well, your body needs protein, that's true. Of course, research has shown that rich people need more protein than poor people, but we all need some.

Well, thanks to some new laws we're gonna

PROTEIN-RICH
KETCHUP

INSTANT
PROTEIN-RICH
TOMATO
SOUP

pass, all Americans can get the protein they need just by breathing and drinking water. There will be plenty of protein-rich material floating around in the air, and the water will be chock full of pure government-approved industrial-grade protein, available to all without charge.

A FUN WAY TO GET
NECESSARY CARBOHYDRATES:
AN ICE COLD
POTATOSICLE!
YUM...

Are Carbohydrates Important?

They sure are! Didn't you ever hear of Vitamin C? If you don't eat enough carbohydrates, Idaho will go out of business. And to make sure you get enough, we are going to print up some new Carbohydrate Stamps, just like the old

CARBO-STAMPS

... AND CARBOHYDRATE STAMPS FRY UP NICE AND CRISP IN A LITTLE PORK FAT OR MOTOR OIL

Food Stamps except that they're made from potatoes. You just eat the stamps! Yum.

Of course, if you eat too much carbohydrate, you'll get fat, but you can always cut down on other types of food.

Isn't it nice how everything balances out.

How can we cut down on Calories?

See, some people can eat all the calories they want and not get fat. Other people eat just a few and put on pounds. So we propose a Calorie Credit that the fat people can sell to the skinny people just like tax credits.

Now, this is a brilliant idea that I thought of when I was governor of California...

...and if it doesn't work it's the Democrats' fault!

OK... last question...

What's the fastest way to quickly Lose Weight?

Just stop eating!
And that's where our diet is best! Because with the Reagan Diet the terrible temptation to eat is gone. There's simply no food, so there's no temptation.

You'll see quick results, not only at home, but at school also.

Let's take a look at our new School Lunch Program first...

Special
School Lunch
Section

Schools are where our eating habits are formed, so what better place to begin a diet? Students should be alert and ready to learn. Light lunches keep them awake, but heavy food makes them... um...

.Major breakthrough in school lunches...

SLOPPY JOE
BUN COVERED BY HAMBURGER
IN SAUCE. AN OLD SCHOOL
LUNCH RECIPE REPLACED BY

NEAT JOE

How the new lunch saves tax dollars

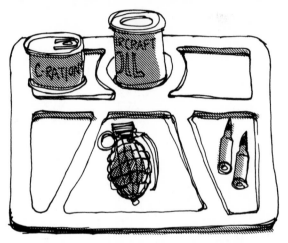

OLD LUNCH WITH FOOD

COSTLY CHICKEN, PEAS,
POTATOES, BREAD, MILK,
COOKIES, FRUIT.

NEW LUNCH WITHOUT FOOD

MONEY BETTER SPENT
ON GRENADES, BULLETS,
OIL AND C RATIONS...

Old American Favorites

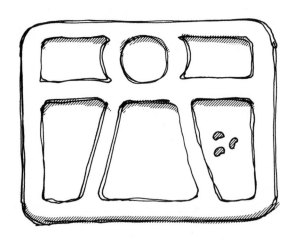

THREE-BEAN SALAD

LOW-CALORIE CHICKEN

Choice of Hot or Cold Lunch

COLD CHEESE LUNCH

HOT CHEESE LUNCH

Getting back to more natural foods

<u>HOT DOG</u>
HIGHLY PROCESSED MEAT
MADE UP OF BEEF LIPS, HEART,
TONGUE, LUNGS... REPLACED WITH

<u>NATURAL FOOD</u>
THE SAME INGREDIENTS
IN THEIR NATURAL STATE.
GREAT FOR DIETS, EH?

THEY'RE NOT JUST FOR SMOKING, ANYMORE...

Monday:
Cigarette Soup

AND THANKS TO GOVERNMENT SUBSIDIES, TOBACCO IS ALWAYS IN PLENTIFUL SUPPLY AND LOW IN COST.

Tuesday: Newspaper Lasagna

WITH LAYERS OF NUTRITIOUS
SURPLUS CHEESE AND KETCHUP.
ONE SUNDAY PAPER FEEDS A
FAMILY OF FOUR FOR A WEEK.

Wednesday:
Baked New Jersey

JUST LIKE BAKED ALASKA BUT
MORE REFINED. USE ONE OLD TIRE
TUBE AND ICE CUBES. A GLAZE OF
10 W 30 AND PURE IMITATION TOPPING.
THEN LEAVE IN BRIGHT SUN 'TIL
GOLDEN BROWN. AS GOOD AS
ITS NAME.

Thursday:
Throw Rug Flambé

A HANDY QUICK MEAL
WHEN THE POWER COMPANY
HAS TURNED OFF YOUR LIGHTS.

Friday:
Baked Stuffed Keds

ONE OF THE MOST PIQUANT OF ALL THE
RECIPES. A FAVORITE WITH KIDS.
STUFF WITH CHEESE, WHITE BREAD AND
OLD SOCKS. A TRADITIONAL
MEATLESS ENTRÉE.

Saturday:
Chili con Nada

LOW IN CALORIES BUT HIGH IN
TASTE. A SOUTHWESTERN
FAVORITE. GO EASY ON THE
CHILI 'TIL YOU'RE USED TO IT.

Sunday:
Corned Beef and
Cabbage Surprise

THE TRADITIONAL IRISH DINNER
NOW EVEN MORE REALISTIC.
CHECK IT OUT.

Shish Kabob can be made with any old thing

Making French Croissants

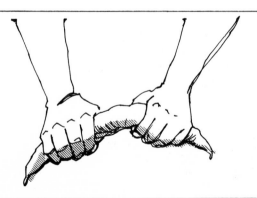

Ketchup Pizza (Extra thin corrugated crust)

Refried Tea Bags

KEEP
HEAT
LOW

Aids for the Serious Dieter

NOW YOU WON'T HAVE
TO STARVE YOURSELF.
WE'LL DO IT FOR YOU!

Keep fresh fish in the diet

Only 110 calories per goldfish

Acid Rain: A Tangy, Low-Calorie Salad Dressing

New Yogurt Flavors make dieting even easier

Cheese-fattened rats make good eating

SEND FOR ALL-NEW
DEPARTMENT OF
AGRICULTURE
PUBLICATION,
"The Urban
Rat Farm,
A Guide for
Homesteaders"
GPO # 411 71-7117-3

Firm, pink marbled flesh...

Even a good breakfast can be economical and

Slimming (For example: Hamsters and Eggs)

And here's how Ice Cream lovers can lose weight...

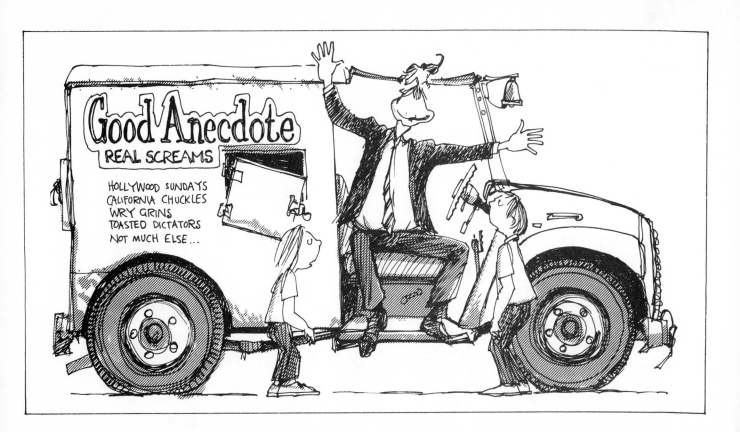

Fried. Naugahyde Chips

Crispy Snacks for school lunches

Naugahyde Fly-away Birds

HEALTH NOTE

NAUGAHYDE
DOES NOT
PROMOTE TOOTH
DECAY

Leftovers? Naugahyde needs no refrigeration.

Stop eating junk food. Eat junk mail.

And Bathwater! An important source of protein.

New trends in Diet Foods

Dieting used to be expensive.

Special light foods always cost more. But now you don't need light beer, light wine or light bread.

Now all you need is...

Hard-boiled L'eggs for salads

SURPLUS CHEESE

1.

2.

3.

4.

5.

6.

ultra low calorie, high bulk.

Eat like the beautiful people on a budget

SEMI-SOFT SHEETROCK DIP

DESIGNER WATER

100% HORSE MEAT

FILLY MIGNON

MEDALLIONS OF PAINT ROLLER

And here's Grandma's contribution to the table...

New Poster helps dieters

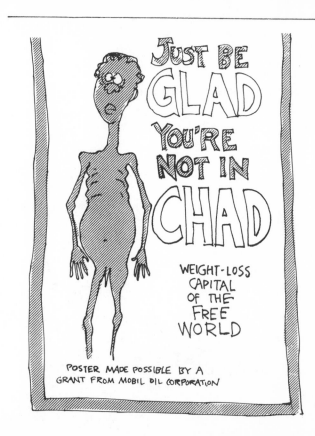

3. Get a snack down at the old Post Office.
(Sticks to ribs.)

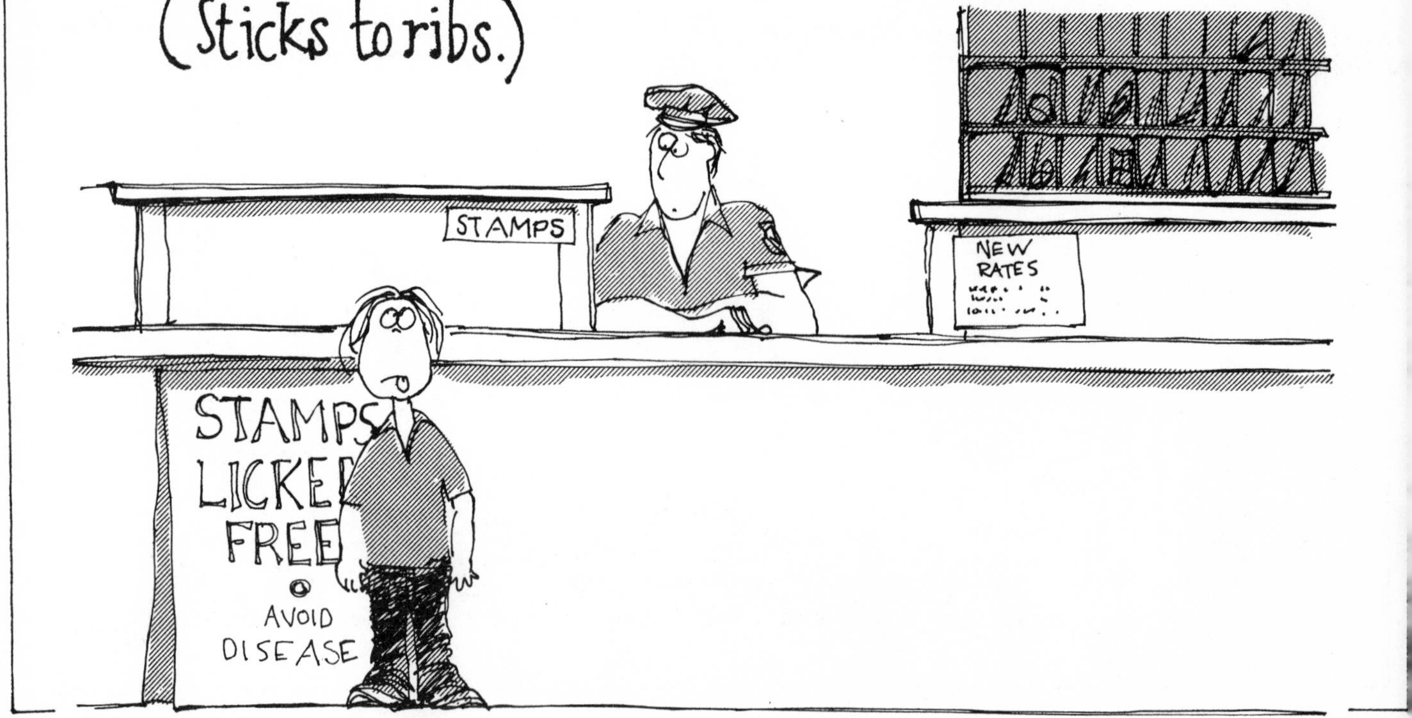

and in closing...

A Dieter's Grace

... and that even these, the least of thy children, will be able to... uh... GOOD HEAVENS! Look at the time! I'm late for dinner at the White House!